THE WEAPONS ENCY

TANK AIRCRAFT AFV SHIP ARTILLERY VEHICLES SECRET WEAPON

TWE-005 EN

 PANZER III Sd.Kfz. 141

THE WEAPONS ENCICLOPÆDIA

EDITORIAL STAFF

Luca Cristini, Paolo Crippa.

REDAZIONE ACCADEMICA

Enrico Acerbi, Massimiliano Afiero, Ruggero Calò, Flavio Chistè, Anna Cristini, Carlo Cucut, Robert Duncalf, Salvo Fagone Enrico Finazzer, Björn Huber, Andrea Lombardi, Aymeric Lopez, Marco Lucchetti, Luigi Manes, Giovanni Maressi, Francesco Mattesini, Alberto Peruffo, Maurizio Raggi, Andrea Alberto Tallillo, Antonio Tallillo, Massimo Zorza.

PUBLISHED BY

Luca Cristini Editore (Soldiershop), via Orio, 35/4 - 24050 Zanica (BG) ITALY.

DISTRIBUTION BY

Soldiershop - www.soldiershop.com, Amazon, Ingram Spark, Berliner Zinnfigurem (D), LaFeltrinelli, Mondadori, Libera Editorial (Spain), Google book (eBook), Kobo, (eBoook), Apple Book (eBook).

PUBLISHING'S NOTES

LICENSES COMMONS

CONTRIBUTORS OF THIS VOLUME & ACKNOWLEDGEMENTS

We thank the main contributors to this issue: The profiles of the floats are all by the author. Photo coloring is by Anna Cristini. Special thanks to national and/or private institutions such as: Army General Staff, State Archives, Bundesarchiv (wikipedia/ CC-BY-SA 3.0), Nara, Library of Congress, etc. A P. Crippa, A. Lopez, L. Manes, C. Cucut, Tallillo archives. Model Victoria (www. modelvictoria.it), for making available images or other of their archives.
Special thanks to "Minstrel" who edited the corrections of the English text.

For a complete list of Soldiershop titles, or for every information please contact us on our website: www.soldiershop.com or www. cristinieditore.com. E-mail: info@soldiershop.com. Keep up to date on Facebook & Twitter: https://www.facebook.com/soldiershop. publishing

Titolo: **PANZER III SD.KFZ. 141** Code.: **TWE-005 EN**
Series edited by L. S. Cristini
ISBN code: 978-88-93278799. First edition September 2022
THE WEAPONS ENCICLOPAEDIA (SOLDIERSHOP) is a trademark of Luca Cristini Editore

THE WEAPONS ENCYCLOPÆDIA
TANK AIRCRAFT AFV SHIP ARTILLERY VEHICLES SECRET WEAPON

PANZER III
Sd.Kfz. 141

LUCA STEFANO CRISTINI

BOOK SERIES FOR MODELLERS & COLLECTORS

SOLDIERSHOP PUBLISHING
ILLUSTRATED HISTORY

CONTENTS

▲ Tank Panzerkampfwagen III Ausf.L (Sd.Kfz. 141/1) at Bovington UK (Wikipedia).

INTRODUCTION

The **Panzer III**, short for its full name of **Panzerkampfwagen III**, whose identification number within the German Army was **Sd.Kfz. 141**, was designed from the analysis of the operational experiences gathered from its two predecessors: the Panzer I and II. Thanks to receiving the full support of the German General Staff, the vehicle soon became the main battle tank of the Panzer-Divisions for a number of years, replacing in the front line role from1940 onwards the light and under armed Panzers 1 and 2 who were moved to training and reconnaissance roles as well as providing a chassis for various self propelled mounts. The Panzer III, produced in nearly 6,000 vehicles and in 12 different models and many more subsidiary versions, was steadily improved over time by upgrading the main armament and thickening the armor with spacing plates, and constituted in the early part of World War II the mainstay of the German Panzer-Divisions that dominated the battlefield. The J version, equipped with a 50 mmKWK 39 L/60 cannon,as the most powerful installed in the Panzer III was able to counter even more powerful vehicles, including the T34 and brought some respite to the Panzer Forces, but was the maximum size allowed by the turret ring. A short 75mm Kwk L/24 was installed in the Mark N having become available from up gunning of the Panzer 4 but even, with special ammunition was not an ideal weapon due to it's low muzzle velocity. However, by 1943, the Panzer III was almost obsolete and was relatively easy to defeat in battle, where the volume and increased firepower of allied vehicles was becoming very apparent. As a consequence the Germans needed to develope heavier tanks, superior, in a quality versus quantity argument that would also be capable of being upgraded. The Wehrmacht was therefore forced to gradually withdraw it from the front line, but was able to make use of its reliable chassis and drive components in producing large numbers of Assault Guns, turretless vehicles that could be equipped with powerful weapons that could fulfill some of the tank fighting role at lower cost particularly when on the defensive. The chassis was also used for other specialist vehicles and in reality there were still some Panzer 111 tanks in service until the end of the war in Europe.

▲ Tank Panzer III Ausf. D. Operation fall Weiss the invasion of Poland, September 1939. At this stage of the conflict the tanks are all in official feldgrau. Bundesarchiv (Coloring by the author).

▲ Tank Panzerkampfwagen III Ausf.B (Sd.Kfz. 141/1), Bundesarchiv (coloring by the author).

■ THE DEVELOPMENT

Germany's defeat in World War I, and the resulting Treaty of Versailles imposed on Germany, prohibited the country itself from owning or manufacturing weapons such as tanks or military aircraft. However, the Germans had learnt valuable lessons from that war and new doctrines emerged that would be implemented when the Second World War began, that initially were far advanced from French and British strategic thinking. The Germans also in the mid 1920's were able to train with and make use of Soviet facilities particularly at Kazan in training and exercising even with the limited types of vehicles it gave an opportunity to develope tactics and experience in using large mobile forces. The Soviets also had reasons to cooperate arising from their experience of the British and French in supporting White forces in the Russian Revolution, this cooperation had almost ceased by the time of the election of the new German Chancellor in January 1933 but was useful in developing the theory and principles of the new Panzerwaffe as well as giving the Soviets an opportunity to overhaul their own battle doctrine under the brilliant "Red Napoleon" Marshal Tukhachevsky feted to die in he Stalinist Purge of 1937. During the spring of 1935, in great secrecy, the *Heereswaffenamt* ("Army Armaments Office") set specifications for two new types of tanks that would go to equip the nascent armored divisions. The first vehicle was to be armed with an anti-tank gun and two machine guns, while the second was to be an infantry support vehicle armed with a larger caliber gun capable of assisting the infantry in destroying fixed targets. The first later became known as the Panzerkampfwagen III was to be a standard medium tank for the light companies of a tank battalion, intended for the destruction of opposing armored vehicles. The second heavier one would become known as Panzerkampfwagen IV. At the time to maintain secrecy the covert name assigned, for the Panzer III,was *Versuchskraftfahrzeug* 619, Mittlerer Traktor ("Prototype 619 medium tractor") so as to confuse enemy observers.

The specifications for the vehicle were as follows:
- maximum weight of 15 tons;
- fully tracked;
- maximum speed of 40 km/h;

▲ Panzer III Ausf L. Bundesarchiv assembly lines.

▼ Preproduction model of the Panzer III Ausf.B, recognizable by the typical drive train. Bundesarchiv.

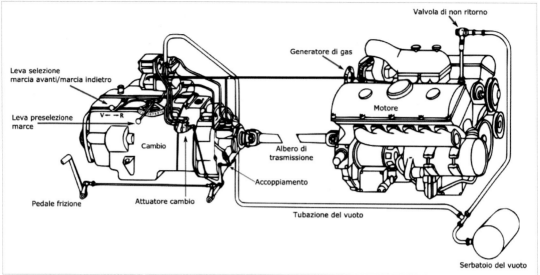

Valvola di non ritorno
Generatore di gas
Motore
Leva selezione marcia avanti/marcia indietro
Leva preselezione marce
V — R
Cambio
Albero di trasmissione
Accoppiamento
Pedale frizione
Attuatore cambio
Tubazione del vuoto
Serbatoio del vuoto

▲ Diagram of Maybach-Variorex engine and gearbox installation. Wikipedia by Antonioptg.

- crew of five men;
- thicker armor on the front;
- 37-mm cannon in a rotating turret as main armament;
- light machine guns as secondary armament;
- radio equipment for medium-range communications.

The requirements of the combat vehicle were that it needed to take into account the load-bearing capacity of the road bridges, have a five-man crew, and the installation of a radio system to allow communication internally and with other tanks and at the command level. Armor protection was to be heavier in the front than in the rear, as the new vehicle was to be used in the forward elements of assaulting tank formations. The vehicle was to be operated by a crew made up of commander, gunner and loader in the turret, and the driver and radio operator at the front of the hull. The Panzer III turned out to be the first of the German tanks to be equipped with an intercom system for communications within the tank using throat microphones. Following this, all Panzers were equipped with this device, which proved very effective in combat and of considerable benefit in maintaining tactical control.

From the very beginning a vigorous debate broke out over the type of weapon to be assigned to the vehicle and there was a dispute between Guderian himself, who was pressing for the adoption of a 50mm gun, and the Armaments Office, which considered the 37mm fieldpiece to be sufficient especially as the infantrywere already equipped with the same anti-tank weapon, the famous PaK 36, and this would enable good use of ammunition in service for re supply. Those in the armaments office won the day, but Guderian nevertheless ensured that the turret also be designed from the outset for possible mounting of heavier weapons, which happened later, enabling the tank to stay in front line service.

Having resolved this thorny issue, contracts were awarded for the construction of prototypes and test vehicles. The most suitable German manufacturers with excellent reputations in production efficiency such as MAN AG, Daimler-Benz, Rheinmetall and Krupp were chosen. After a further two years of study and testing, the example proposed by Daimler-Benz was approved. Potential builders such as Ford and Opel despite a strong German presence were excluded because they were partially American-owned, although Henry Ford shared many of the views of the new Regime.

■ TECHNICAL CHARACTERISTICS

The design of the PzKpfw III consisted of four elements: hull, turret, front superstructure with the opening for the turret, and rear superstructure with the engine compartment fitted with armored hatches for powerplant maintenance. Each section was welded with appropriately shaped steel plates and all four were riveted together. The hull was divided into two main compartments separated by a bulkhead. The forward compartment housed the gear train and steering mechanism, the combat chamber housed the driver, equipped with appropriate external vision systems, and a gunner who also served as a wireless operator, and the rear compartment housed both the combat and engine compartments. The turret was inserted on top of the circular opening with a ring mounted with roller bearings, superstructure and crew arrangement remained unchanged throughout the production of the Panzerkampfwagen III. The hull, made of welded steel plates, the thicknesses of which underwent an increase with each variant put into production contrasted with the bolted construction of Italian, British and French tanks of the time and gave some protection to the crew from shearing and spalling.

■ TURRET AND ARMAMENT

The turret of the first version was built by assembling the plates by bolting, but already welding the plates was preferred as on all later models. On the roof was placed, slightly to the side, the armored observation cupola for the tank commander, a detail subject to continuous evolution over the course of the service models due to battlefield experience. Over time it would change from a simple cylindrical superstructure to a sophisticated cupola, and equipped with several viewers that provided a good 360-degree view. The turret housed not only the commander but also the gunner and gun loader. The commander's and

▼ View of the engine of the Panzer III Maybach HL 120 mit 300 PS. Wikipedia by Benutzer Stahlkocher.

gunner's seats were both attached to the turret wall. The gunner found accommodation to the right of the main gun. For external observation he had a glass block-protected opening and external hatch on the right side of the turret. A similar observation hatch was located on the left side of the turret for the gunner. The gunner rotated the turret with a crank and the gun fired through an electric control system. The machine gun, on the other hand, was mechanically operated by a foot pedal.

Both the machine gunner and the gunner each had a side exit hatch located on the sides of the turret. The commander sat in a higher position in the center of the turret, directly behind the main gun, and had access to the tank from a cupola at the top with two access hatches, equipped with five observation ports protected by glass blocks and steel rails.The commander had an additional control on the right side to assist the gunner with turret movements if needed. There was also a turret position indicator for the crew. Emergency exit was possible on both sides of the tank hull, but was removed from the M version onward.

■ PANZER III RADIO SYSTEM

The tank driver sat in the left front, position next to the gearbox and the instrument panel mounted above it to his right. The observation slot available to him was, again, protected by an armored glass block and hatch forming a visor which could be fully closed for protection. When shutdown, the driver looked through a periscope equipped with corner mirrors, for which two holes had been drilled in the hull above the visor. He had another observation opening on the left side, also protected by a glass block and an external tab. The radio operator, on the other hand, sat in the front right position, using a head-rest to move the machine gun housed in a ball structure at the front of the hull. The radio equipment he operated consisted of two receivers mounted to his left above the gearbox and a transmitter mounted in front of him under a panel.

The radio was a Funkgerät 2 consisting of two receivers and a transmitter and with a 2-meter-high whip antenna mounted on the right side of the structure that could be retracted inward, and connected to a switch that could directly transfer communications to the tank's intercom. Only the commander, driver, and radio operator were equipped with a headset and throat microphone and thus connected to the radio system and, it was possible for the commander and the operator to be on two different lines, for example, one on the internal intercom and the other on the command level radio circuit. To obviate this potential problem and ensure internal communication, both had a red and green light bulb in their field of view, which they could turn on by a predefined signal sequence. The commander communicated directly by voice with the gunner and loader.

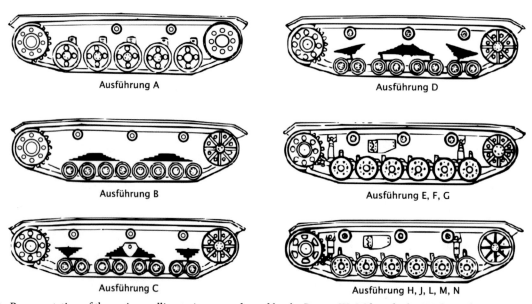

Ausführung A

Ausführung D

Ausführung B

Ausführung E, F, G

Ausführung C

Ausführung H, J, L, M, N

▲ Representation of the various rolling train types adopted by the Panzer III. Wikipedia by H.Klawuttke

Starting with the L version, the tank was equipped with a special sound device that allowed the commander and gunner to communicate with each other in case of particularly loud internal noise. There was also an observation port on the right side of the radio operator's station. The driver and radio operator did not have separate access hatches, and to gain egress from the vehicle they had to enter and exit through the commander's route.

◼ ENGINE AND GEARBOX

The engine up to the E version consisted of a Maybach HL 108 TR 12-cylinder V-engine with a displacement of 10,838 liters, for a maximum power output of 250 hp at 3000 rpm, allowing a maximum speed of 40 km/h. The engine was mounted at the rear in a longitudinal position; on each of the two sides of the engine were housed the two gasoline tanks, a battery, and a radiator. The cooling fan located behind the engine occupied the entire width of the compartment and provided effective cooling. The engine transferred power through a shaft to the gearbox assembly arranged at the front of the hull. The transmission had six forward and one reverse gear. Fuel was supplied through two carburetors, and the range of the early versions was 165 kilometers. Fuel for the A, B and C versions was contained in two tanks totaling 125 liters, while from the D version two new tanks were added increasing the total capacity to 320 liters of gasoline. The gasoline engine from the F version onward was a 300-hp 12-cylinder Maybach HL 120TRM of similar characteristics to the TR but more modern and efficient and was built by Norddeutschen Motorenbau GmbH. To the left and right of this centrally mounted engine were the fuel tank, battery, and water radiator. Behind the radiators were the fans. Starting with the H version, the hydraulic pressure clutch mounted up to that time was replaced by a three-disc dry clutch. The first three models of the E, F and G series used a Maybach Variorex gearbox with a preselector transmission, which contained ten forward gears and one reverse gear. To shift gears, the driver simply had to depress the clutch pedal after selecting a gear using the shift lever to activate the automatic transmission. This advanced but complicated gearbox, which was difficult to maintain in the field, was replaced by a six-speed synchronized gearbox starting with the H version. Connected to the gearbox was the cone drive with the steering apparatus,

▲ Engine compartment tank of a Panzer III from a Verlinden model.

the steering of which was done with two steering levers acting on the hydraulically assisted internal shoe brakes. Power passed through side gearboxes on the outside of the hull to the track drive wheels.

■ SPECIAL MODIFICATIONS

The tanks used in the North African campaign were equipped with tropical equipment. For this purpose, cooling power was expressly increased by redesign of the cooling system to increase flow and the air filter was supported by a felt bellows filter located outside the engine compartment under the armor protection to cope with the sand and dust. From 1943 onward, all newly produced Panzerkampfwagen IIIs, or those subject to refurbishment, were equipped with a close protection projector mounted on the turret sides in the light of experience during the Russian campaign and the headlights became removable. In the same year, the improved *Fliegerbeschussgerät* 42 came into use, which was attached to the commander's cupola by clamping screws and could accommodate both the MG 34 and MG 42. A protective Zimmerit covering, designed to prevent the attachment of adhesive magnetic charges, was also made available to the vehicles; the procedure was discontinued in September 1944. Beginning in 1944, tanks used on the Eastern Front received so-called Ostketten, i.e., widened tracks with an external "beak" that decreased the ground pressure of the tank, allowing it to move betterover snow or muddy terrain and reducing the risks of bogging, but the benefit was limited due to the design of the track. Beginning in 1943, 5-mm-thick plates, so-called schürzen, "tank skirts," were mounted on the sides of the vehicle and around the turret to protect it from mainly hollow-charge projectiles, in combat these were often torn off and many tanks mounted incomplete sets after short periods in action.

▼ Panzerkampfwagen III Ausf.M displayed in the Panzermuseum in Munster, Germany. Wikipedia by Baku 13.

▲ An Ausf. D during the invasion of Poland in 1939. Bundesarchiv.

▼ Panzer Command Vehicle III version D1 with extensive antenna equipment and ring antenna on engine compartment, France 1940. Wikipedia by OBZWAR.

▲ Two Panzer III Ausf. J of the 14th Panzer Division at Poltawa, Russia, autumn 1942. Bundesarchiv.

▼ A Panzer III Ausf. J in the boundless steppes near Stalingrad in Russia. September 1942. Bundesarchiv.

VERSIONS OF THE VEHICLES

There were numerous versions of the Panzer III service models were made from A to N, as well as specialist vehicles in small production runs, such as flamethrowers. In the later years of the war the basic hull and drive train still made a great contribution to supporting hard pressed infantry by providing them with anti tank support in the form of the Sturmgeschutz with a capable long barrelled 75mm main gun. The first four models of the Panzer III, called pre-series, were the Ausf. A, B, C and D (where Ausf. is short for *Ausführung*, meaning "model" or "version" in German). These early versions were all produced by Daimler-Benz in the years from 1936 to 1939. The main armament consisted of a 3.7-cm KwK 36 gun, already used by the PaK 36 antitank guns and here modified for its use on armored vehicles. As secondary armament there were three MG 34 machine guns: two coaxial in the turret and the third arranged in the hull and for use by the radio operator. Protection for the hull and turret was only a maximum of 15 mm thick. Weight varied, for the first 4 models, from 15.4 tons of the Ausf. A, to 16 of the Ausf. D.

Panzer III Ausf. A: designed for a five-man crew. Like all versions of the first series it had a track and transmission system that over time showed problems that were only solved from the E series onward. Produced in very few units, they were permanently withdrawn by 1940.

Panzer III Ausf. B: practically a copy of the Ausf. A, it introduced a few variations to the turret and tracks in an attempt to improve them. Few units (15) were made of this model, which were also withdrawn in early 1940.

Panzer III Ausf. C: with this model, the search for a solution to the still defective drive train continued, but without achieving effective results. Few units were produced and the model met the same end as its predecessors.

Panzer III Ausf. D: later changed to the final identification number Sd.Kfz. 14, it was the last pre-series model (always still with the intention of obtaining an effective drive train), which continued to be a

▲ Panzer III E, a command tank marching on the Balkan front in 1941. Bundesarchiv (coloring by the author).

source of concern for the crews. The cupola was made more functional, armored with 30 mm steel and remained in use until the F version of the Panzer III. The maximum armor thickness was also increased for the hull from 15 to 30 mm. The D series was produced in fifty-five units. Like all previous models it was withdrawn in February 1940.

Panzer III Ausf. E: it was the first series model of the Panzer III with the muchinproved drive train, however, only forty units were made. By establishing the minimum armor at 30mm, this brought the weight to nearly 20 tons, and it was thus equipped with a more powerful engine. In addition to Daimler-Benz, Henschel and MAN AG were given production orders. The gearbox was improved and access with the addition of hatches on both sides of the hull and the opening visor for the radio operator. Delivered to the Panzer Divisions from January 1940, the Ausf. E participated in all wartime operations until 1943, including the French and Balkan campaigns and fatefully in Operation Barbarossa were the limitations of the tank became increasingly clear. Some of the tanks were rearmed with a better gun and upgraded to F standard.

Panzer III Ausf. F: from this model of the Panzer III the main production of the vehicle that would serve the German army began. Very similar to the E version, changes were made to the turret and engine. 435 vehicles were built between October 1939 and June 1940. In mid-production the main armament was

▲ Panzer III observation tank version for artillery in the Soviet Union: the turret is protected by *Schürzen*. Bundesarchiv (author's coloring).

▲ An Ausf. L of the SS-Panzergrenadier-Division "Wiking" (note the divisional symbol above the tank's right track) advances into the Soviet steppes in June 1942. Bundesarchiv (coloring by the author).

upgraded to a 5 cm KwK 38 L/42 with external mantle, a modification later extended to all Ausf. E and F available. It fought in France, North Africa, the Balkans and the Soviet Union. The gun itself was a considerable improvement over the 37mm and allowed the use of a high explosive round in infantry support.

Panzer III Ausf. G: very similar to the Ausf. F and just slightly longer than that version, in 1940 it was produced in 600 units against an initial order of 1,200 units, later reduced due to the arrival of the Panzer 38(t) of Czechoslovakian origin. The Ausf. G was progressively armed with the more powerful 5 cm KwK 38 L/42. Other modifications saw the addition of a new cupola taken from the Panzer IV and the Fahrersehklappe 30 visor with hatch on hinges for the driver; late production units mounted 400 mm wide tracks. The G series was the first to be equipped with *Rommelkiste* ("Rommel's box"), a container attached to the rear of the turret to improve stowage for the crew. The G version was employed from the spring of 1940 in all major war theaters.

Panzer III Ausf. H: the continuous increase in weight of the tank was beginning to cause ground pressure problems. The Army Armaments Office, together with the manufacturing companies, considered modifying the drive train by retaining the formula already adopted on the Ausf. E, enlarging the track width from 36 to 40 cm. The same armament was retained but the armor was significantly improved with additional 30 mm spaced plates, achieving now 60 mm on the front and rear of the hull and on the front superstructure; the rear of the turret was also completely redesigned. All these changes brought the weight to almost 22 tons. The model was produced in about 450 units.

Panzer III Ausf. J: a very successful model with a length of 5.52 meters and a height increased to 2.50 meters, the Ausf. J had its armor increased to 50 mm. Demonstrated to the Führer in April 1941, the J version was produced in as many as 1549 units. In mid-production the tank was equipped with the more powerful 5 cm KwK 39 L/60 gun. Between 1941 and 1942 Krupp built as protopype a new version, the Ausf. K, by combining the J-series hull with the turret of the Panzer IV, but the experiment did not go beyond this stage and no series production was carried on.

Panzer III Ausf. L: just as the Germans were adopting the 50 mm KwK 39 as the main weapon of the Panzer III, the sloping armor of the Russian tanks forced German tactics into much closer combat to achieve results. Given this tactical situation, it became necessary to increase the Panzer III's armor to allow for closer engagement where Russian marksmanship which was generally poorer would be more dangerous. The production of the new model reached a total of about 1,300 units. The new version featured increased armor and the weight increased to 22.3 tons. On the commander's cupola of the Ausf. L a mount with two articulated arms was installed, suitable to accommodate an MG 34 in anti-aircraft configuration as well as a group of *Nebelkerzen Wurfgeräten* projectors, each with its own non-adjustable swing and elevation, and which fired smoke grenades at about 30 meters from the tank, secured to each side of the turret for some close quarter protection. Finally, Schürzen were tested for the first time on Panzer IIIs. These were additional 10mm-thick armored plates mounted on both flanks and all around the turret to minimize the effects of hollow charge anti-tank weapons such as bazookas or the dreaded Soviet anti-tank guns. The Ausf. L, considered an elite weapon, went to equip the armored regiments of the 1. SS-Panzer-Division "Leibstandarte SS Adolf Hitler", the 2. SS-Panzer-Division "Das Reich", the 3. SS-Panzerdivision "Totenkopf" and the Panzergrenadier-Division "Großdeutschland", but they were also distributed to the army's armored divisions.

Panzer III Ausf. M: last version of the Panzer III to mount the KwK 39 L/60 while solutions were still being sought to improve the Panzer III's armament. The Ausf. M was produced in just over 1,000 units. It appears, however, that only 250 of these became M tanks while most of the already completed chassis were used as the basis for the StuG, Ausf. N or the Flammpanzer IIIs. Improvements to the new tank were aimed primarily at enhancing tank operations on the Eastern Front, although it was also used in Tunisia and Sicily. The Panzer III Ausf. M had its baptism of fire in Tunisia and continued in service until the end of the war, participating widely in the Battle of Kursk and the defense of Sicily, often equipped with the *Schürzen*.

PANZER III AUSF E TANK, POLAND 1939

▲ Panzer III E of the German Armed Forces used in Operation Fall Weiss (invasion of Poland). Note the full white cross used only at the beginning of the war-Poland September-October 1939.

Panzer III Ausf. N: this was the last series of the Panzer III and mounted a 7.5 cm KwK 37 L/24 gun, found in the early versions of the Panzer IV. The use of this weapon on the Ausf. N entailed a downgrade of the Panzer III at the tactical level, as it was now no longer a fully fledged combat tank but an infantry support vehicle, the KWK 37 being basically a howitzer with a low muzzle velocity especially suited to containing enemy infantry attacks and destroying fixed positions such as machine gun nests. Production took place from June 1942 to August 1943 and about 700 were completed, virtually all derived from hulls of older models. All units produced from March 1943 onward were equipped with Seitenschürzen and Zimmerit antimagnetic paste, but because of the heavy weight of the KwK 37 gun they had no additional armor. Apparently, studies and plans were made for a hypothetical Ausf. O, but there is no evidence that such a version of the Panzer III existed.

■ OTHER SPECIALIST VERSIONS

Flammpanzer III (Sd. Kfz. 141/3): the fierce street fighting that was taking place at Stalingrad in1942 prompted the Germans to build a flamethrowing tank based on the Panzer III to clear out Soviet defenders from buildings. About a hundred of these vehicles based on the Ausf. M were produced. The flame lance 1.50 meters long, could fire eighty bursts lasting two or three or seconds within a useful range of 36 meters. The front of the hull was reinforced by a 30 mm thick plate to provide additional protection when approaching the target. The Flammpanzer III was operated by a crew of only three men, the commander was in charge of operating the flamethrower and MG 34 in the turret, while the other machine gun was operated by the radio operator and the vehicle weighed 24 tons. Between March and December 1943 the new flamethrower vehicles operated in the Soviet Union and also in Italy.

Tauchpanzer ("submersible tank"): it was a futuristic vehicle designed in anticipation of Operation Sea Lion, the landing in England planned for the summer of 1940. Unlike what the Allies did later in 1944, the Germans trialled a tank capable of traveling several kilometers underwater at a maximum depth of 8 meters and at a speed of 4-6 km/h. These *Sonder-Panzerabteilung* were to be equipped with Panzer II, III and IVs capable of operating underwater. Various tank conversion kits were devised for this purpose, which required total waterproofing of the fighting compartment. The air needed by the crew and engine apparatus was supplied by an 18-meter-long hose secured to a surface buoy supporting a 1.50-meter-high breathing tube. Daimler-Benz modified less than a hundred units of Panzer III between Ausf. F, G and perhaps even H. Safety problems that appeared during testing made the vehicle extremely unpopular among the crews, which consisted of selected volunteers. When it became clear that Operation Seelowe would never happen, almost all Tauchpanzers were equipped with a special 3.5-meter-long snorkel for fording rivers. Most of these ended up being used during the invasion of Russia for crossing the Bug River, after which they were used as regular tanks.

Bergepanzer: several Panzer IIIs were converted into recovery vehicles known as *Bergepanzer*, a practice that continued during the conflict by using the hulls of tanks that had been recovered from the front line; in total there were 271 conversions. The vehicle, lacking the turret and part of the superstructure, had a box-shaped wooden structure mounted and, was capable of towing heavy vehicles less than 25 tons, but the crane with which it was equipped often proved to be insufficient for the task.

Fahrschulwanne: some Ausf. F were converted into school tanks (*Fahrschulwanne*) by replacing the turret with a glazed structure that allowed for group driving school lessons.

Minenräumpanzer: again fbased on the Ausf. F, prototypes of a minesweeper tank (*Minenräumpanzer*) were made: the vehicle featured a reinforced drive train and a significant increase in both lower hull and side armor. The turret was removed and a roller type minesweeping device was attached to the front.

PANZER III AUSF F TANK, FRANCE, JUNE 1940

▲ Panzer III F of the 4th Panzer-Division 35th Regiment, 2nd Company, 1st Platoon, Tank 3 during Operation Fall Gelb - French Campaign in June 1940.

Transportpanzerkampfwagen: utilizing early model Panzer IIIs, three types of transport tanks (*Transportpanzerkampfwagen*) were produced between 1943 and 1944 in the same way as the Bergenpanzer, that is, by removing the turret and mounting a wooden superstructure over the hull. Their purpose was to make the Schlepper III, the Munitionspanzer III and the Pionierpanzerwagen III (used by military engineers). A total of about 150 tanks of all three types were converted and used exclusively on the Eastern Front.

Schützenpanzerwagen ("armored infantry vehicle"): manufactured in a very limited number of units, again for the Eastern Front only. The vehicle, lacking a turret, could carry a squad of Panzergrenadier into battle and is the only example of a Panzer adapted for tactical infantry transport during World War II by the Germans although the Canadian Ram usefully served late war Allied forces.

Eisenbahnwagen: a particular variant of the Panzer III was the Schienen-Kettenfahrzeug SK 1, built in two or three units in late 1942 on the Ausf. N. It was able to move on rails and was used to provide mobile heavy support to German Anti-Partisan units in countering the Russian "War of the Rails". The speed could reach up to 100 km/h.

▲ Rare photo of a radio command tank covered with branches and foliage. Eastern Front, 1943.

▲ General Hermann Balck (standing left in the cupola) in a Panzerbefehlswagen III Ausf. H Command version tank at Pandelejmon, Greece, on April 16, 1941. This vehicle is equipped with a fake 37 mm main gun and a fake MG 34 coaxial machine gun, but it has a real MG 34 machine gun mounted on a ball on the right side of the turret(shel)l. Note the presence of a newly taken prisoner New Zealand soldier next to the two Mk III Panzers of the 2nd Panzer Division. Bundesarchiv.

OPERATIONAL DEPLOYMENT

OPERATIONAL HISTORY OF THE PANZER III

The various models of the Panzer III were used in combat in large numbers until the second half of 1943, when the combat power of the vehicle declined in the face of more modern and heavily armed and armoured opposing vehicles on all fronts. The later, more up-to-date versions, nevertheless continued to serve until in the last year of the war, used mainly in the rear but occasionally met in combat.. The Panzer III justly remains famous in the history of warfare for the very advanced and modern design coupled with the tactical use of it's experienced crews that gave the Germans dominance over their opponents until the middle of the War. It was a true symbol of the Blitzkrieg!

■ INVASION OF POLAND (FALL WEISS), SEPTEMBER 1939

On September 1, 1939, with the German invasion of Poland, World War II began. On that day, the Panzer-Divisions could only count on less than 100 Panzer IIIs of all models in service at that time (98 to be precise); their impact was therefore not decisive, numerically outnumbered in armored regiments by more dated Panzer I and Panzer II. Meanwhile, increased production had made it possible to raise the number of Panzer IIIs per company from three to five. The model version used against the Polish army were the least performing: the bulk of the pre-series production from A to D. Much better was the performance of the Ausf. E and F, along with the aforementioned light Panzer I and II and the very few Panzer IVs, all distributed over six Panzerdivisions, with 2,400 tanks in all. In this campaign the most destructive work was done by the Luftwaffe, and the tanks were supposed to take care only of the second-line infantry and the rear. This was not the case since the Poles sold their lives bravely, and if the 37 mm cannons of the Panzer IIIs were sufficient against almost all Polish tanks, their "thin" armor was certainly not immune to the Polish anti-tank weapons either, which proved to be very effective. The Czech-made 47 mm cannon, the UR anti-tank guns, the locally made 20 mm Swiss Solothurn, or the 7T main gun and the 37 mm Bofors, which were all effective anti-tank weapons, took a heavy toll of Panzer IIIs during the conflict. In total, the Germans had more than 16,000 casualties and lost as many as 217 tanks and many more were disabled and later repaired.

▲ A panzer III advances unstoppably in the Russian campaign. Bundesarchiv (author's coloring).

■ INVASION OF NORWAY: APRIL-JUNE 1940

A few Panzer IIIs of the D version then participated in the Norwegian campaign between April and May 1940 as part of *Panzer Abteilung z.b.V. 40* ("armored detachment for special duty 40"). They then remained in Norway with the occupation troops until Germany's unconditional surrender, formed into the *Panzerbrigade "Norwegen"*. During the so-called "drole de guerre" as the French called it (the phony war), the warring parties took advantage of that kind of truce to settle down into in activity. However the early months of the war following the invasion of Poland were not quiet everywhere, particularly in the Baltic Area as the consequences of the Molotov Ribbentrop Secret Protocols played out and the Soviet Union attacked Finland. The Panzer III had no part to play in that conflict but the Finns provided the Germans with data and characteristics on Soviet tanks engaged in the operations. To Norway (as mentioned) a detachment of about 30 Panzer III Ausf.C and D was sent, camouflaged with brown stripes, more than enough force to counter the small Norwegian army. Denmark, in turn was also invaded, offered almost no resistance, and the Panzer III never encountered any real opposition. In Norway, the French and British expeditionary forces had almost no tank support, and the Luftwaffe once again proved equal to the task.

■ THE WAR IN THE WEST MAY-JUNE 1940

On May 9 the *Drole de guerre* ceased and a full stage assault broke loose in the West. The Germans, having had plenty of time for meticulous organization, attacked the much-vaunted French force which showed all its limitations especially in the skies where the Luftwaffe proved vastly superior in combat. However, the French armored forces, with the addition of the well-trained and well-armed British Expeditionary Forces (BEF), should have been more than equal to the Wehrmacht.

The Germans swept through Belgium and Holland meeting little organized resistance and the key fortress guarding the Meuse river Eben-Emael, the cornerstone of the Belgian defense, fell under a daring attack by German Paratroops. Everywhere here the German advance was swift and coordinated, despite setbacks from some Allied divisions giving strong counter attacks to the Panzer force, by May 14 a few days later Belgium was beaten and, despite determined opposition, capitulated on May 28.

▼ Tests designed to verify the potential of the Submersible Panzer (submarine), Tauchpanzer III in the English Channel area in anticipation of the invasion of Britain in 1940. Bundesarchiv (author's coloration).

PANZER III AUSF F FRANCE SUBMARINE TANK FOR OPERATION SEELÖWE, SEPTEMBER 1940

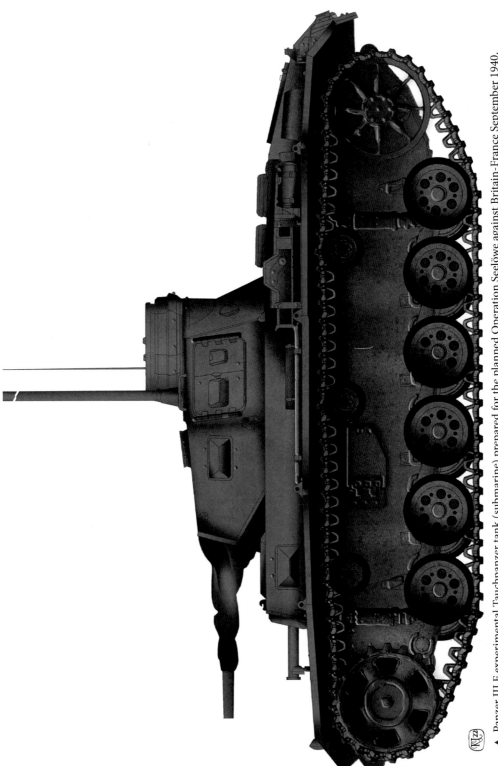

▲ Panzer III F experimental Tauchpanzer tank (submarine) prepared for the planned Operation Seelöwe against Britain-France September 1940.

▲ Panzer III L with additional protection and bomb throwers in Italy 1943. Bundesarchiv (coloring by the author).

PANZER III AUSF E TANK COMMAND 21ST PANZER DIVISION, NORTH AFRICA, SUMMER 1941

▲ Panzer III E command of the 21st Panzer-Division 5th Regiment with mock cannon and lacking MG in casemate. Equipped with Fu6 (short wave) and Fu8 (medium wave) radio systems. In landed version color feldgrau. Added camouflage in yellow-brown will be applied later. Africa Korps in Libya, August 1941.

■ THE BATTLE OF FRANCE (FALL GELB) 1940

The French forces were confident that they would still contain the German assault as in 1914. Even many German generals were doubtful given the fierce resistance of the French Army in World War one , but not "blitzkrieg theorists" such as Guderian, sponsor of the Panzer III who believed he understood the strategic weakness arising from French defensive measures typified by the Maginot Line. They were the ones who conceived *Fall Gelb* (Yellow Case), a surprise attack through the dense forest of the Ardennes, the weakest point of the French defense but believed impassable for a mass attack. German armored forces were to be decisive, served by a better road network than the defense planners appreciated and supported by the most effective use of air power to date with almost total air superiority gained early on.

At the time of the attack on France, the German army had 390 Panzer IIIs (mainly Ausf. E and F) and Panzerbefehlswagen, command tanks Panzer IIIs assigned to the tactical commanders of armored formations to lead the units directly to the battlefield. A small number of Panzer IVs armed with 75 mm guns were also available. On paper, the Allies were significantly better off, both numerically and qualitatively. In direct tank clashes the Germans would in practice only have Panzer IIIs at their disposal, all armed with the 37 mm gun although during the French campaign tanks of the F version, armed with the shorter 50 mm gun also appeared for the first time. Despite technical and numerical inferiorities, the Panzer III achieved great successes during the French campaign: the German crews were the best trained in the new doctrine of mobile warfare primarily made up of combined tactics between tanks, anti-tank guns and dive bombers followed up by infantry to take and hold captured positions and clear out pockets of enemy ressistance. The sophisticated and effective radio system mounted on the panzers demonstrated it's full potential in directing forces to the most advantage. From the very first clashes with the French, the Germans easily got the better of the more powerful but badly directed and led enemy tank forces.

However, the Panzer IIIs had serious problems when their main gun proved insufficient to pierce enemy armor such as British and French heavy tanks for example the Matildas and Char B1s, suffering locally some significant losses, in total in France while triumphing everywhere, the Germans lost 135 Panzer IIIs out of a total of almost 800 armored vehicles lost and damaged and suffered 160,000 losses among their soldiers,of which around 27,500 were killed.

■ WAR IN NORTH AFRICA (1941-1943)

General Erwin Rommel's legendary Afrikakorps entered combat for the first time in the spring of 1941 with a main armored force consisting of Panzer IIIs, specially outfitted for the African theater, both

▲ Panzer III Ausf. G number R03 in North Africa, spring 1941. Bundesarchiv (coloring by the author).

TANK PANZER III AUSF J AFRIKA KORPS, TUNISIA, LIBYA, 1942

▲ Panzer III J with long barrel of the 21ˢᵗ Panzer- Division. 5ᵗʰ Panzer Regiment, 1ˢᵗ Company 3ʳᵈ Platoon, Tank 2. Sand yellow camouflage version with Grun brau color. Note on the back a metal canister holder, used by tankers to place everything in it.

▲ Panzer III Ausf. H v. command of General Georg von Bismarck. North Africa, 1942. Bundesarchiv (coloring by the author).

PANZER III AUSF. J, CAUCASUS 1942-43

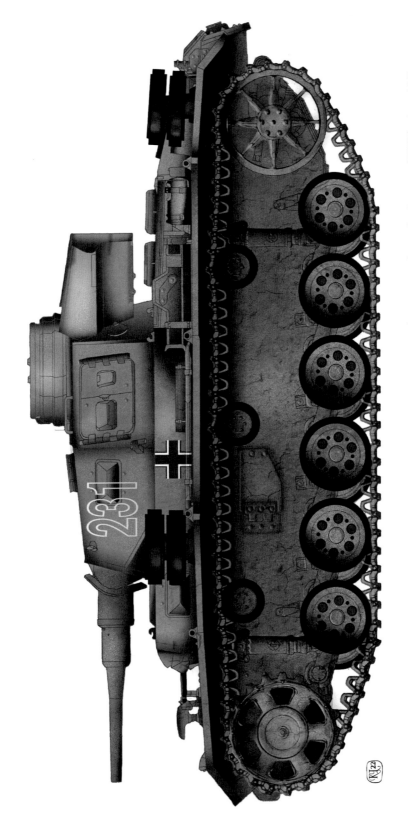

▲ Panzer III J of the 5th SS Panzer-Grenadier-Division "Wiking" 5th Regiment, 2nd Company, 3rd Platoon, Tank 1 in the Caucasus (USSR) winter 1942-43. This company boasted the presence of ace Karl Jauss who was awarded the German Gold Cross in 1944.

equipped with the 37mm anti-tank gun and the 50mm L/42 gun. Here too, as in France, the danger proved to be the British Matilda tank and its 2 pounder/ 40mm main gun. The German Panzers fought consistently well in the desert, where their speed, combined with the tactical brilliance of the "Desert Fox," proved unbeatable in an even combat. But continued losses and few available replacements led to an increasing weakening of the Panzer III complement and the German armored force in general. The desert environment proved to be particularly harsh for the vehicles. Breakdowns, due to heat and sand with few replacements available due to a hostile Mediterranean to cross, with Malta and Gibraltar in particular allowing the interruption of supply routes and priority given to the Eastern Front, meant the campaign was always difficult for German forces to decide conclusively.

German triumph however regularly occurred during the Battle of Ain el-Gazala, where the Afrikakorps fielded, alongside the Italian Allied forces, 223 Panzer IIIs between Ausf. G, H and J or L equipped with the more effective 50 mm cannon. The British far more numerous and also equipped with new American tanks, suffered in a month their most bitter defeat in the desert. The winning combination this time turned out to be the combination of panzer and 88 gun in an anti-tank role wreaked havoc on the British armored forces. Shortly before El Alamein, the Germans received the first Panzer IVs with the long 75 mm cannon, putting the Panzer IIIs on the second line. Nevertheless, still after the defeat at el-Alamein, Rommel had 164 Panzers in Libya. Before being captured or destroyed by the overwhelming Allied forces, the Panzer IIIs (J and L) of the two AK Panzer-Divisions deployed in Tunisia managed to achieve one last victory at the Battle of the Kasserine Pass against inexperienced American forces.

■ OPERATION BARBAROSSA: ASSAULT ON THE SOVIET UNION

On June 22, 1941, Hitler triggered the assault on Soviet Russia. Eleven of the seventeen German Panzer-Divisions deployed east for Operation Barbarossa, had about 1,500 Panzer IIIs, about 950 of which were versions equipped with the good 50-mm cannon. Together there were another 500 Panzer IVs. By contrast, at the beginning of the war, the Red Army fielded nearly 20,000 tanks, but this impressive armored fleet consisted mainly of light and medium tanks of mediocre efficiency and technically outdated and the Soviet Officer Corps had been effectively destroyed in Stalin's purges leaving few competent senior officers to resist the invasion. However, a thousand T-34s and about 500 KV-1s, which were superior to all German vehicles in protection and armament, were also available. The German tank guns were more than sufficient against the tens of thousands of BT-7s and T-26s that made up the bulk of the Russian armored forces. However, German crews discovered that both the KV-1 and T-34 were immune to their fire even at short range if armed with the 37mm and usually the short 75mm L/24. Despite their enormous numerical preponderance, the Soviet armored forces were almost completely annihilated

▲ Deployment of Panzer III Ausf. M in Russia 1943. Bundesarchiv (coloring by the author).

during the first months of the war by the vastly more experienced and disciplined German Panzer-Divisions supported strongly by the Luftwaffe. There are reports of the destruction or capture of more than 17,000 Soviet tanks. During operations, even the T34, when faced at less than 1,000 meters, suffered some damage from the Panzer III's 50mm gun particularly if hit on the thinner side armour. The only invulnerable Soviet vehicles were the KV-1s. The German General Staff tried to solve this problem by introducing more effective guns and ballistically innovative ammunition in larger calibers, however, during 1942 the great bulk of armor was based on new Panzer IIIs in numbers approaching 2,000.

Later also came the 7.5cm L/24 cannon now mounted on the Ausf M and N but with limited muzzle velocity and a shortage of good ammunition for anti tank combat. By 1943 the Panzer IIIs were outnumbered by the new Soviet tanks even though they were still present at Kursk in nearly 500 units.

Historians still debate the events of Kursk but from then on the Panzer111 would be replaced at first gradually, by the introduction of the Tigers, Panthers and long gun armed Panzer 4 able to interrupt Soviet mass tank attack and offensives. Many of the withdrawn Panzer III's then being used for conversion to Assault Gun or other roles. By late 1944 only 79 units of Panzer III's were still operational on the Eastern Front.

■ FINAL PHASE: THE DEFENSIVE WAR (1944-1945)

The last versions of the Panzer III, the Ausf.M and N, were markedly different machines from the early Panzer III models. The much improved protection, adequate armament, etc. meant that particularly against Western Forces a well trained crew could give a good account of themselves. By mid-1944, Daimler-Benz engineers succeeded in mounting the 75 mm low-velocity gun on the N version, which was to be the final variant in the Panzer III's long service history.

By then, the old Ausf.J-M tanks that had survived the Eastern Front were diverted to the Italian front, along with other veteran models from Africa. The long-barreled 50mm L/60 was still able to penetrate the armour of the tanks opposing it in Italy where due to the terrain, ambush and very strong defensive works reduced opportunities for the mobile warfare of the Eastern Front Some improved Ausf.J and M fought in limited numbers even in Normandy, but their movements were limited by Allied air supremacy. However, once again, as in the Villers-Bocage clash it was shown that the Panzer III was still equal to most Allied tanks. By the end of 1944, however, the Panzer IIIs had effectively ended their service life. Few vehicles remained operational and there was no realistic way for further improvement of the vehicle, given the Panzer IV performed all the tank fighting roles better and production of all combat vehicles was now declining in the face of strong aerial and ground assault.

Nevertheless, the Panzer III, like the Stuka and the 88 gun, will remain an iconic symbol of the German Blitzkrieg and gave good service until almost the end of the War.

▲ Panzer III Ausf. L captured by the Russians 1943 (coloring by the author).

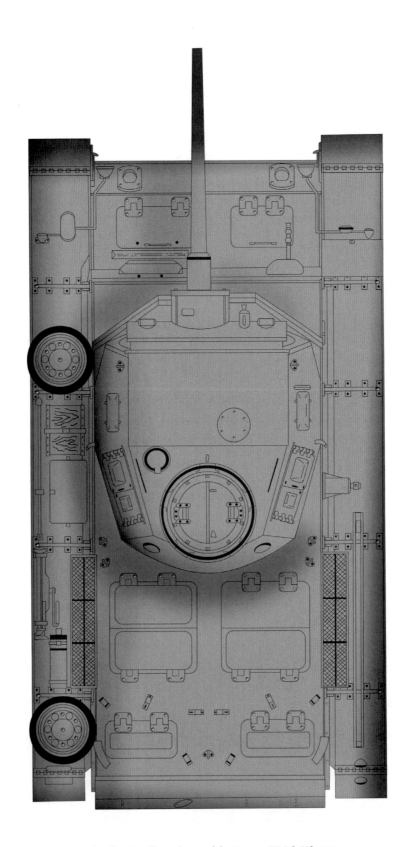

▲ Profile view from above of the Panzer III Sd. Kfz. 141.

TANK PANZER III AUSF J SS DAS REICH, KHARKOV 1943

▲ Panzer III J of II panzer regiment of SS Division "Das Reich," 2nd Battalion of SS-St. Sturmbannführer Christian Tychsen (1910-1944) decorated with RitterKreuz with oak fronds (small photo). Kharkov (USSR) March 1943.

▲ Panzer III advance between the fields of Ukraine during the Russian invasion. August 1942, Bundesarchiv (coloring by the author).

▼ Panzer III Ausf. M flamethrower version no. 411. Operational in Russia 1943. Bundesarchiv (coloring by the author).

TANK PANZER III AUSF L AFRIKA KORPS, TUNISIA, FEBRUARY 1943

▲ Panzer III L with short barrel of the 15th Panzer- Division. 2nd Company 3 Tank Platoon 2. Camouflage version at the Battle of Kasserine in Tunisia in February 1943.

PANZER III Sd.Kfz. 141

TWE | 37

▲ View of the Panzer III tank Sd.Kfz. 141 from the front and back.

▲ A Panzer III Ausf. M nr. 102 of the 25th Panzer regiment of the 7th panzer Divison during Operation Citadelle. Russia, early July 1943. Bundesarchiv (coloring by the author).

PANZER III AUSF L TANK OF THE SS PANZER DIVISION TOTENKOPF USSR, MARCH 1943

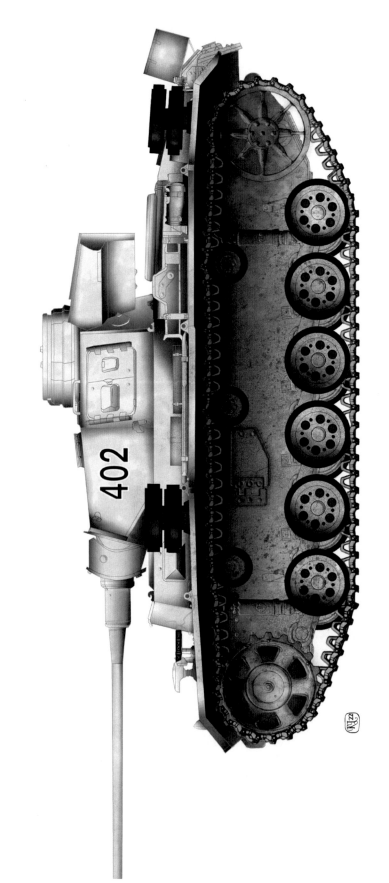

▲ Panzer III Sd Kfz 14171, the long barrel of SS Panzer-Division Totenkopf. From 4th company, command platoon, tank 2. White winter camouflage. Operational in the Kharkov area (USSR), March 1943.

CAMOUFLAGE & DISTINGUISHING MARKS

In the early stages of the war in Poland and France, the German army mainly used vehicles painted in Dunkelgrau (RAL 7021), with some vehicles also painted in Dunkelbraun (RAL 7017) as a camouflage (motif) until the Oberkommando des Heeres decided that only Dunkelgrau should be used. The decision affected not only tanks, but also all AFVs, including armored cars, half-tracks and even the mobile canteen vehicles were painted the same color.

This Dunkelgrau is often shown in illustrations incorrectly. The point is that it was in reality a very dark bluish-gray color. This error occurs due to the fact that gray tends to "blend" effectively with the surrounding colors and consequently appear much lighter.

The war, however, opened the eyes of Hitler's generals, especially in Russia and Africa, where both theaters of operation Dunkelgrau could be spotted miles away, a clear invitation to enemy fire. Therefore, German divisions in the USSR used any useful material to color their vehicles more effectively including natural materials such as chalk, bedding, piled snow until the inevitable whitewash was available. The resulting camouflage saved the lives of many tank crew. These ad hoc coverings also had the advantage that they gradually washed out with the late winter and the early spring rains. In Libya, although white was not needed, there was a lot of trouble in finding a good solution but with typical German thoroughness, eventually a solution was found ,when Gelbbraun (RAL 8000) was sent to the North African Front and the vehicles in Dunkelgrau were quickly recamouflaged with the desert colouring. In addition to coloring in Gelbbraun, Graugrün (RAL 7008) was also used in Africa, the latter in different variants frequently conditioned by what the tankers had on hand, or what they managed to capture from the enemy.

Since 1942, official colors began to become scarce at the front and often at the factory as well. Military vehicles were therefore painted using alternative color schemes from whatever was available, especially for the desert vehicles which never received their full complement of supply, due to Allied naval and aircraft interdiction of supply convoys, however schemes using Braun (RAL 8020) and Grau (brown and gray, RAL 7027) were often met on the battlefield. In the pages of the book you will find as clear images as possible of these colors and their RAL designation. Apart from Africa, vehicles painted in the two-tone camouflage already in use in the desert also began to be used on the Eastern Front.

It should be remembered, however, that by mid-conflict most German tanks in Russia were still Dunkelgrau, at least until 1943, when the OKH issued a new order that the standard base color of all vehicles became Dunkelgelb (dark yellow, RAL 7028). The color was not a true yellow, but rather tended toward bronze. A delicate color anyway, which varied enormously, depending on many factors: who painted it, how much it was diluted with solvents, weather, wear and tear, etc. RAL 7028 offers, even in the bibliography, a large number of "variations". So it was partly by chance, partly by luck that they came up with that modern camouflage that the Germans called the *Hinterhalt-Tarnung* or "Ambush." A complicated aspect to describe, but in fact it is an effect of light filtered through natural foliage, in short, a very effective camouflage.

WW2 GERMAN TANK &AFV COLORS & CAMOUFLAGE

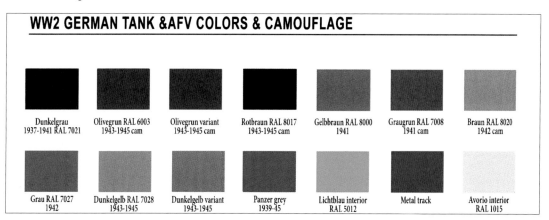

Dunkelgrau 1937-1941 RAL 7021	Olivegrun RAL 6003 1943-1945 cam	Olivegrun variant 1943-1945 cam	Rotbraun RAL 8017 1943-1945 cam	Gelbbraun RAL 8000 1941	Graugrun RAL 7008 1941 cam	Braun RAL 8020 1942 cam
Grau RAL 7027 1942	Dunkelgelb RAL 7028 1943-1945	Dunkelgelb variant 1943-1945	Panzer grey 1939-45	Lichtblau interior RAL 5012	Metal track	Avorio interior RAL 1015

Just as in works of art, one could also speak of styles, as varied as possible so that one was similar to that of the *pointillisme* of the French Impressionists, and another took the form of disc or mottled. The choice of one style or the other was also in a way the signature of the factory that produced the vehicles as from mid-1944 the vehicles were painted in the production plants. Factory-applied colors were a base of Dunkelgelb, with flecks of Rotbraun a red brown and Olivgrün an olive green. More and more problems arose with storage, thunderstorms and general events which made the outgoing supply varied.

Finally, in December 1944, a new order was issued that the tanks were to be painted all over with a base coat over the red-oxide primer consisting of Dunkelgrün and/or Olivgrün with applications of Dunkelgelb and Rotbraun stripes and spots, and this appears to be the last order given for camouflage while the war was in progress.

The application of camouflage was generally done with airborne paint sprays, failing which it was done "the old-fashioned way", using brushes, mops, or simply rags on the end of a stick. These techniques and the make do and mend attitude that typified later war German forces vastly increases the camouflage variations that would later be destined for the battlefield.

Like all armies, the German army understood from its vast battle experience that concealing vehicles in defensive or offensive postures would increase the odds of surviving the encounter. Therefore, in addition to camouflage painted on the vehicle itself, foliage (branches, bushes, hay, even woodpiles) was often used to cover the vehicle, usually from the front, to make it even more difficult to detect and distinguish from its surroundings. More rarely, tarpaulins and camouflage cloths and nets mixed with foliage were also used to further conceal the tank. Not least, mud and snow were also an inexpensive, but effective, camouflage that was very useful in blending in with the surroundings.

▲ A tanker intent on coloring the camouflage of his vehicle (an Sd.Kfz 173) with spray. Bundesarchiv.

TANK PANZER III AUSF N AFRIKA KORPS, TUNISIA, SPRING 1943

▲ Panzer III N with the latest model of short-barreled cannon of the 15th Panzer- Division. 2nd Company 1 tank platoon 2. Tunisia campaign, spring 1943.

▲ Most of the Tauchpanzers intended to invade Britain were then equipped with a special 3.5-meter-long snorkel for fording rivers. Most of these then ended up being used during the invasion of Russia (Operation Barbarossa) for crossing the Bug River, after which they were used as regular tanks. Bundesarchiv (coloring by the author).

▼ Panzer III Ausf. J radio command version in Russia September 1941. Bundesarchiv (coloring by the author).

TANK PANZER III AUSF M PANZER DIVISION HERMANN GOERING. SICILY, JULY 1943

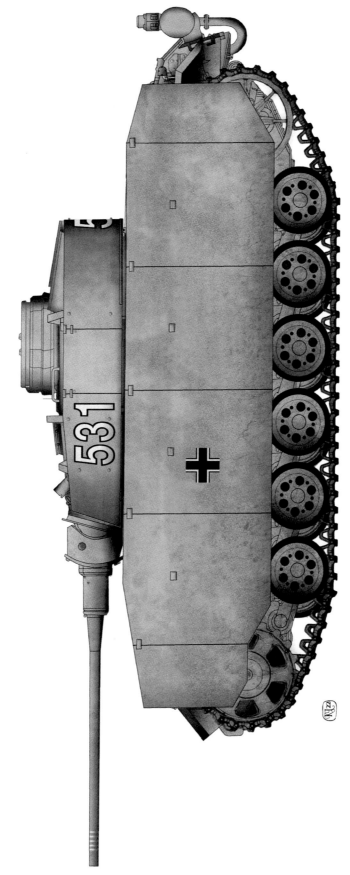

▲ Panzer III M of the Panzer Division of Luftwaffe chief Hermann Goring. In Italy the division was under the orders of Marshal Kesselring. This tank equipped with Schürzen belonged to the 5th Company, 2nd Platoon (Abteillung) first tank.

PANZER III AUSF M TANK OPERATION ZITADELLE-BATTLE OF KURSK. USSR, JULY 1943

▲ Panzer III M of the Panzer Division. Tank without side protection number 234 (2nd Company, 3rd Platoon, tanks 4) of the 15th Panzer Regiment of the 11th Panzer-Division present at the Battle of Kursk.

PRODUCTION AND EXPORT

Since 1936, after Daimler-Benz initiated the project, the German firms assigned to build the Panzer III in all its versions were: the Alkett, FAMO, Henschel & Sohn, MAN AG, MIAG, Waggonfabrik Wegmann and MNH; manufacture lasted from late 1936 to August 1943 and totaled about 5,700 units.

OTHER USERS

The Panzer III in all its many was mainly used by the German army but also by the various other countries indicated below, among allies and enemies who captured the vehicles during the war usually used it for support roles such as supply delivery and towing.

ALLIES:

- **Bulgaria** - Received 10 Panzer III Ausf. N for the *Bronirana brigada*.

- **Croatia** - Bought some Panzer III Ausf. L and Ausf. N.

- **Italy** - The Royal Army received from Germany in 1943 a dozen Ausf. N (as well as an equal number of StuG III Ausf. G) to equip the 1st "M" Armored Division, but the vehicles never entered action with Italian forces and after the armistice of September 8 returned to German units.

- **Romania** - Received 11 Ausf. N given in force to the *Divizia 1 Blindată*.

- **Slovakia** - The Germans ceded to the Slovak armed forces 7 Ausf. N.

- **Turkey** - Ordered a batch of 56 vehicles but the ongoing war prevented the transaction, although perhaps 20 or so were delivered.

- **Hungary** - Was the first among the Allied countries to receive Panzer IIIs, 10 units, given in force to the Magyar armed forces deployed on the Eastern Front.

- **Japan** - The Japanese government purchased two Panzer IIIs from their German allies during the war (one with a 50-mm gun and one with a 75-mm gun), for the stated purpose of studying their technology, which in the Land of the Rising Sun was highly advanced on the air and naval front but lacking on tanks. However, by the time the vehicles were delivered, Panzer III technology was obsolete.

ENEMIES:

- **Czechoslovakia** - After the war it operated a small proportion of Panzer IIIs, including four rebuilt flamethrower vehicles.

- **Norway** - After the war made use of about 32 ex-German units; most of the vehicles were decommissioned from active service beginning in 1951.

- **Soviet Union** - Two Panzer IIIs were sold to the Soviets in 1940, during the period of the USSR-German alliance (following the Molotov-Ribbentrop pact), and were used by the Soviets for comparative tests with early T-34 units.

During the war, the Russians managed to capture and reuse several Panzer IIIs. In July 1945 there were still 31 units in service and 67 under repair.

After the Battle of Stalingrad, the Red Army seized a large number of Panzer IIIs, which, as they could no longer be used as combat vehicles due to their now inadequate armor and armament, were put back into service as light fighters under the designation SU-76i, removing the turret and replacing it with a 60-mm thick armored casemate armed with the Soviet 76.2-mm anti-tank gun.

▲ Panzer III Ausf. J in the Stalingrad area where the reversal of the Nazi armies began. Bundesarchiv (coloring by the author).

▼ Panzer III Ausf. J belonging to the 24th Panzer Division in the Don/ Stalingrad area Russia summer of 1942. Bundesarchiv (coloring by the author).

▲ Panzer III Ausf. J nr 2 on the eastern front. January 1942. Bundesarchiv (coloring by the author).

▼ Many Panzer IIIs like this Ausf. N were abandoned in Russia following the retreat. Today many have become a kind of memorial to that war in the parks of many Russian towns. Wikipedia.

▲ Panzer III Ausf N with *Schürzen*. Italian Campaign 1943-44. Bundesarchiv (coloring by the author).

▼ Another image related to German armored troops in Italy. A string of Panzer IIIs camouflaged in the vegetation ambushing enemy forces. Bundesarchiv (coloring by the author).

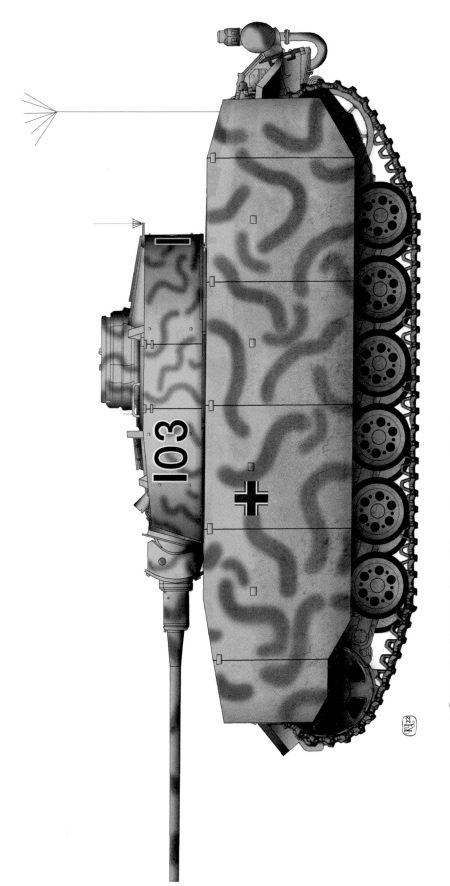

▲ Panzer III M Tank 103 of the 25th Panzer Regiment of the 7th Panzer-Division. Present on all fronts, especially France and Russia. It had among its commanders Erwin Rommel and Hasso von Manteuffel.

PANZER III Sd.Kfz. 141

DATA SHEET

	Ausf. A–C	Ausf. E	Ausf. F, G	Ausf. H	Ausf. J, L, M	Ausf. N
General Features						
Year	A:1937, B:1937 C:1938	1938-39	F: 1939, G: 1940-1941	H: 1940-1941	J: 1941, J/1: 1941-42, L:1942, M: 1942-43	N: 1942-43
Overall Dimensions						
Weight	15 t	19,5 t	20,3 t	21,6 t	22,3 t	23 t
Length	5,69 m	5,41 m	5,41 m	5,52 m	6,41 m	5,52 m
Width	2,81 m	2,91 m	2,92 m	2,95 m	=	=
Height	2,54 m	2,44 m	2,44 m	2,50 m	2,51 m	2,51 m
Armament						
Armament	3,7-cm-KwK	=	5cm Kwk 38L/42	=	5-cm-KwK 39	7,5cm Kwk 37 L/24
Secondary Arm.	3 x MG34	2 × MG 34	=	=	=	=
Ammunition	KwK: 150 MG: 4.500	KwK: 120 MG: 3.600	KwK: 99 MG: 2.000	=	KwK: 78 (J=84) MG: 2.000	KwK: 64 MG: 3 450
Caliber	45	=	42	=	60	24
Weapon length	1.717 mm	=	2.100 mm	=	3.000 mm	1.766 mm
Range	1.000 m	=	1.200 m	=	1.300 m	650 m
Weapon weight	195 kg	=	223 kg	=	255 kg	490 kg
Barrel life	4.000 rounds	=	=	=	8.000 rounds	13.000 rounds
Tank cost	4.800 RM	=	=	=	5.600 RM	8.000 RM
Armor						
Front hull	15 mm/70–80°	30 mm/70–80°	=	30 + 30 mm	50 mm/70–80° (L/M: 50+20 mm)	50 + 20 mm
Side hull	15 mm/90°	30 mm/90°	=	=	=	=
Back hull	15 mm/80°	30 mm/80°	=	30 + 30 mm	50 mm/80°	=
Top hull	18 mm	=	=	=	=	=
Bridge hull	15 mm	30 mm	=	=	=	=
Front turret	15 mm/75°	30 mm/75°	=	=	30 mm/75° (L/M: 57+20 mm)	57 + 20 mm
Side turret	15 mm/65°	30 mm/65°	=	=	=	=
Rear turret	15 mm/78°	30 mm/78°	=	=	=	=
Turret top	10 mm	=	=	30 mm	10 mm	=
Mobility						
Engine (Maybach)	HL 108 TR V12 Moteur Otto	HL 120 TRM V12 Moteur Otto	=	=	=	=
Cylinders	10,84 L	11,87 L	=	=	=	=
Gearbox	5 / 1	10 / 1	6 / 1	=	=	=
Max. speed	32 km/h	40 km/h	=	=	=	=
Reserve	300 l	320 l	=	=	=	=
Autonomy	150 km (road) 100 (elsewhere)	170 km (road) 100 (elsewhere)	=	=	=	=
Width tracks	36 cm	=	=	40 cm	=	=

PANZER III AUSF M FLAMETHROWER TANK 1ST PANZER DIVISION, GREECE, SEPTEMBER 1943

▲ Panzer III M flamethrower version (FL), belonging to the 1st Panzer Regiment of the 1st Panzer Division in Greece in the second half of 1943. Interesting camouflage with color Bruno RAL 8017 on a Dunkelgelb Ral 7028 background.

▲ Panzer III in the Balkan campaign of 1941. Bundesarchiv (coloring by the author).

▼ Panzer III of Panzer Brigade "Norwegen" after the surrender. The three tanks in the front row are all Ausf. N. None of the tanks in this photo appear to show any markings. Bundesarchiv (coloring by the author).

PANZER III AUSF N TANK WITH SCHÜRZEN, USSR, LATE 1943

▲ Panzer III No. One of the last versions to enter production of the Pz III SdKfz 141/2. The special armor added to both flanks and turret served German tanks to defend themselves against deadly Soviet anti-tank guns.

PANZER III AUSF J TANK PANZERBEOBACHTUNGSWAGEN WITH SCHÜRZEN, USSR, JUNE 1944

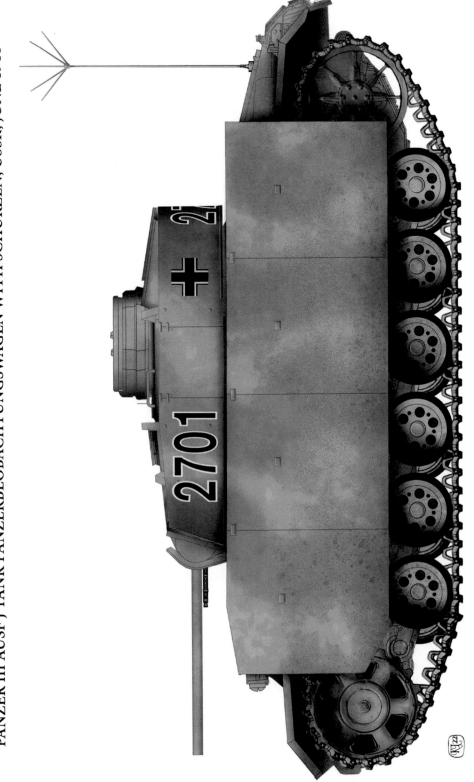

▲ Panzer III J of an unidentified department. Equipped with its false barrel, MG armament, and large antenna. Russian front, late 1944.

TANK PANZER III AUSF J PANZER REGIMENT 21, USSR, JUNE 1944

▲ Panzer III J of the 21st panzer regiment of the 20th Panzer-Division Division. 4th company, 3rd platoon 4 tanks. Operational in the Bobrouisk area (USSR) June 1944.

BIBLIOGRAPHY

· Peter Chamberlain, Hilary Doyle e Thomas L. Jentz, *Encyclopedia of German Tanks of World War Two Revised edition*, Londra, Arms & Armour Press, 1993, ISBN 1-85409-214-6.
· George Forty, *World War Two Tanks*, Osprey, 1995, ISBN 978-1-85532-532-6.
· Philip Greenwood, *Achtung Panzer, No.2, Panzerkampfwagen III*, Dai Nippon Kaiga, 1991.Heinz Guderian, *Panzer General - Memorie di un soldato*, Milano, 2008, ISBN 88-89660-06-6.
· Thomas L. Jentz, Hilary Doyle e Peter Sarson, *Flammpanzer - German Flamethrowers 1941-1945*, Osprey Publishing, 1995, ISBN 1-85532-547-0.
· Robert Michulec, *Armor battles on the Eastern Front (1)*,Hong Kong, Concord pub.company,
· Bruce Calver, *PzKpfw III in action*, Hong Kong, Squadron/signal pubblications, 1988.
· Dennis Oliver, *Panzer German army light tank*, Pen&Sword, Great Britain 2019.
· George Parada, *Panzer IIIAusf L/M*, Photosniper Kagero Polonia 1990.
· Fulvio Miglia, *Le armi del Terzo Reich, il Panzerkampfwagen III*, Roma, Bizzarri, 1974.
· Bryan Perrett, *Panzerkampfwagen III. Medium Tank 1936-44*, Oxford, Osprey publishing, 1999.
· Gordon L. Rottman, *M3 Medium Tank vs Panzer III - Kasserine Pass 1943*, Oxford, Osprey Publishing, 2008, ISBN 978-1-84603-261-5.
· Frido Maria von Senger und Etterlin, *Die deutschen Panzer 1926-1945*, Bernard & Graefe Verlag, 1973.
· Walter Spielberger Spielberger, Friedrich Wiener, *Die deutschen Panzerkampfwagen III und IV mit ihren Abarten*, Monaco, Lehmanns Verlag, 1968.
· Caruthers, Bob *The Panzer III. Pen and Sword. ISBN 9781781592069. 2013.*
· Gander, Terry J. *Tanks in Detail; PzKpfw III Ausf A to N ISBN 0-7110-3015-4.*
· Green, Michael; Anderson, Thomas; Schultz, Frank. *German Tanks of World War II. London, UK: Zenith Imprints. ISBN 9781610607209.*
· Perrett, Bryan. *Panzerkampfwagen III: Medium Tank 1936–44. Oxford, UK: Osprey Publishing. ISBN 1-85532-845-3. 1999.*
· Tucker-Jones, Anthony *Panzer III: Hitler's Beast of Burden. Pen and Sword. ISBN 9781473891081.2017*
· Wolfgang Fleischer *Panzerkampfwagen III. Der Panzer der Blitzkriege. Podzun-Pallas, Wölfersheim-Berstadt 2001, ISBN 3-7909-0732-4.*
· George Forty *Die deutsche Panzerwaffe im Zweiten Weltkrieg. Bechtermünz, Augsburg 1998, ISBN 3-8289-5327-1.*
· Alexander Lüdeke *Panzer der Wehrmacht 1933-1945. 3. Auflage, Motorbuch-Verlag, Stuttgart 2010, ISBN 978-3-613-02953-8.*
· Horst Scheibert *Kampfpanzer III. Podzun-Pallas, Friedberg/H. (Dorheim) 1990, ISBN 3-7909-0393-0.*
· Ferdinand Maria von Senger und Etterlin *Die deutschen Panzer 1926–1945. Bernard & Graefe, Bonn 1998, ISBN 3-7637-5988-3.*
· Walter J. Spielberger *Der Panzerkampfwagen III und seine Abarten. Band 3, 1. Auflage, Motorbuch-Verlag, Stuttgart 1974, ISBN 3-87943-336-4.*
· Walter J. Spielberger, Friedrich Wiener *Die deutschen Panzerkampfwagen III und IV mit ihren Abarten 1935–1945. J. F. Lehmann, München 1968.*
· Jan Suermond *Wehrmacht-Fahrzeuge - Restaurierte Rad- und Ketten-Kfz. 1. Auflage. Motorbuch Verlag, Stuttgart 2005, ISBN 3-613-02513-2.*
· *"Germany's Panzerkampfwagen III, SdKfz 141". World War II Vehicles. Retrieved June 10, 2004.*
· *"PzKpfw III". Achtung Panzer!. Archived from the original on May 10, 2005. Retrieved June 12, 2007.*
· *"Pz. Kpfw.III". Panzerworld. Retrieved April 19, 2005.*

TITLES ALREADY PUBLISHED

TWE-005 EN

Made in United States
Orlando, FL
22 August 2023

36336854R00035